Tom and Bella have a paddling pool on the grass.

1

Bella is sitting in the pool.

She has a bucket.

Bella picks up the bucket and fills it with water.

She holds it up. Oh no!

The water drips out.

Bella lets the water drip
on the plants. Drip, drip.

Then she lets the water
drip on Tom. Drip, drip.

Tom fills up his water gun from the paddling pool.

Tom and Bella have fun in the sun. They get very wet.